There should be 2x12 triangles on the snake's skin. Fill in the missing triangles.

Fill in the missing numbers from the 2x table on the empty leaves above.

Multiply each number in the spider's web by 2 and write the answers in the outer ring.

Find and circle 2x2 differences between these butterflies.

Are there enough red bugs in the picture for each tiny tree frog to catch 2?

Join the dots in the order of the 2x table to finish the flower.

Can you spot 2x4 bees?

...raw lines from the flowers to ...he hummingbirds, so that each ...lculation is joined to its answer.

2x table

These monsters are missing some of their features. Look at their descriptions and draw in any eyes, teeth or fingers they need. Decorate the white monsters' bodies any way you like.

Gruffalump and Peekerpine go to the optician. Whose glasses cost more?

SHMOOZLE

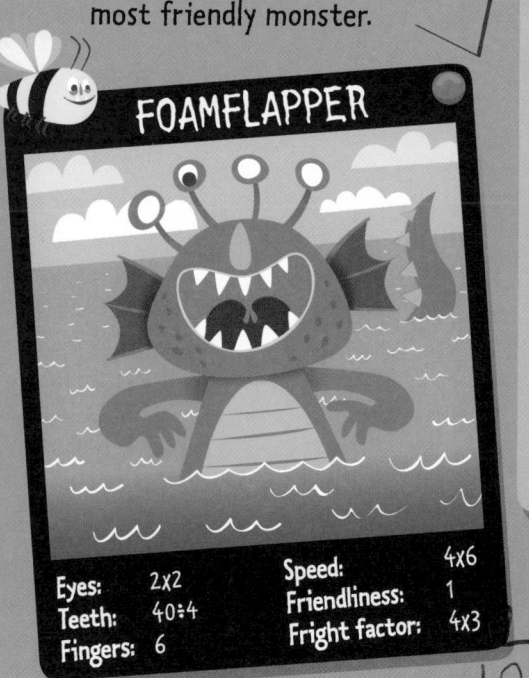

Eyes:	1	Speed:	2x12
Teeth:	2x1	Friendliness:	44÷11
Fingers:	4x3	Fright factor:	2

THE SNOAD

Eyes:	8÷4	Speed:	4x11
Teeth:	11	Friendliness:	12÷2
Fingers:	4x2	Fright factor:	8

GRUFFALUMP

Eyes:	24÷4	Speed:	2x11
Teeth:	2÷2	Friendliness:	12
Fingers:	16÷2	Fright factor:	1

TENTACLE TIM

Eyes:	20÷4	Speed:	2x9
Teeth:	18÷2	Friendliness:	3
Fingers:	4X0	Fright factor:	4

ZAPDOODLE

Eyes:	4	Speed:	4x10
Teeth:	14÷2	Friendliness:	8
Fingers:	4x4	Fright factor:	12÷4

PUFFALONG

Eyes:	2	Speed:	4x7
Teeth:	16÷4	Friendliness:	5
Fingers:	4x2	Fright factor:	28÷4

Draw a smiley face by the most friendly monster.

FOAMFLAPPER

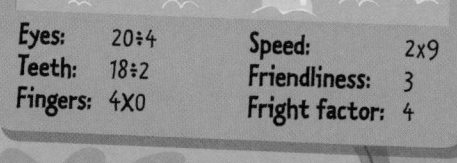

Eyes:	2x2	Speed:	4x6
Teeth:	40÷4	Friendliness:	1
Fingers:	6	Fright factor:	4x3

RAZORCHOPS

Eyes:	8÷2	Speed:	4x5
Teeth:	2x10	Friendliness:	4÷2
Fingers:	10	Fright factor:	2x5

WIGGLESWORTH

Spot 2x2 monster wasps.

BEETLEBAT

Eyes:	6÷2	Speed:	4x12
Teeth:	8	Friendliness:	4x1
Fingers:	2x8	Fright factor:	5

Tentacle Tim, The Snoad and Razorchops have aching teeth. Who's the grumpiest?

PEEKERPINE

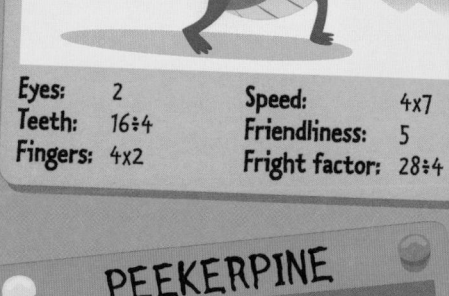

Eyes:	8	Speed:	4x9
Teeth:	10÷2	Friendliness:	2x2
Fingers:	2x0	Fright factor:	22÷2

In a race, who would win: Puffalong or Shmoozle?

Eyes:	2 ✓	Speed:	2x7
Teeth:	2x3 ✓	Friendliness:	32÷4
Fingers:	4x8 ✓	Fright factor:	6

Write "AAARGH!" by the monster with the highest fright factor.

2x and 4x tables

The balloons will burst if their numbers are not in the 5x table. Circle the balloons that survive.

How many items are marked with the manager's special yellow "star buy" labels today? 5x _?

If "Camping" has 5x as many customers today as "Gardening" (which has 9), how many customers is that? 40

Doodle 5x3 more cherries on the cakes, then draw 5x2 bows on the presents.
15 14
10

Doyle's Department Store

One window display changes every 5 weeks. How many weeks will it be before all these windows are showing something new? 25

40

5x8 people enter the store. 5x6 leave and then 5x as many come back as are still inside. How many people are in the store now? 100

30

ROSIE

Spot 5x6 red flowers.

If Rosie buys the toys whose prices are in the 5x table, circle the items she'll take home today.

5x table

There should be 10x3 lights twinkling in the roof of the tent. Count the lights, then draw any that are missing.

CIRCUS

Bertram Boffitt's circus stages 10 performances a week. How many shows is that in 4 weeks?

Spot 10x1 balloons and 10x3 stars in the ring.

If there are 10x as many custard pies as clowns, how many is that altogether?

Multiply the numbers on the ends of each weight to see what it weighs. Fill in the missing numbers so that each pair of weights adds up to 10x10.

HUNDREDWEIGHT HARRY

Bertram Boffitt is 10x older than Bonzo, who is 4. How old is he?

BERTRAM BOFFITT

BONZO

If Pip sells 10x as many cartons of popcorn as he has here, how many is that?

PIP

Connect the dots in the order of the 10x table to finish the horse's costume.

10x table

Help the spies discover the hiding place of some top-secret documents. Each puzzle has one or more answers. Use this key to reveal the letters these answers stand for. The first one has been done for you.

KEY

3	=	M	25	=	C
4	=	R	30	=	Z
5	=	A	35	=	T
6	=	N	45	=	U
8	=	H	55	=	D
9	=	B	60	=	O
10	=	I	80	=	P
15	=	S	100	=	L
20	=	E	110	=	Y

The documents are hidden:

U _ _ _ _ _ _ _ _ _ _ _ _ _ _ _ _ _ _

Fill in the missing numbers from the 5x table on the stepping stones.

Agent C finds 10x2 coins in the fountain and divides them by the number of benches.

Agent B counts some ribbons tied to a lamppost and multiplies the number by the number of lampposts.

Agent D multiplies the number of letters in NEWSPAPERS by the number of newspapers he finds.

1. Find Agent A, then help him and his team solve the puzzles on the paths, whose answers reveal the route as well as part of the coded message.

Circle Agent E's number that's in both the 5x and the 10x tables.

Spot 5x3 spies in the scene.

The number of differences between this real identity card and the fake is 25 ÷ _ ? Can you find them?

2. Now, do the other five puzzles on the page, collect the six numbers and unscramble the coded word to complete the message.

Psst! What's 5x7?

5x and 10x tables

AGENT A

9x5

55

45

40÷5

30

40

45

2÷5=4
20

5x7

35

80÷10

45 (U)

60÷10

8

20

5

40÷10

4

AGENT C

AGENT B

40

9

8

AGENT D

7

60

5

30÷5

6

55

55
25 20
38

10x2 2

90÷10 20

32

3

6x

5x11

65

AGENT E

10x3

30

5x4

20

35

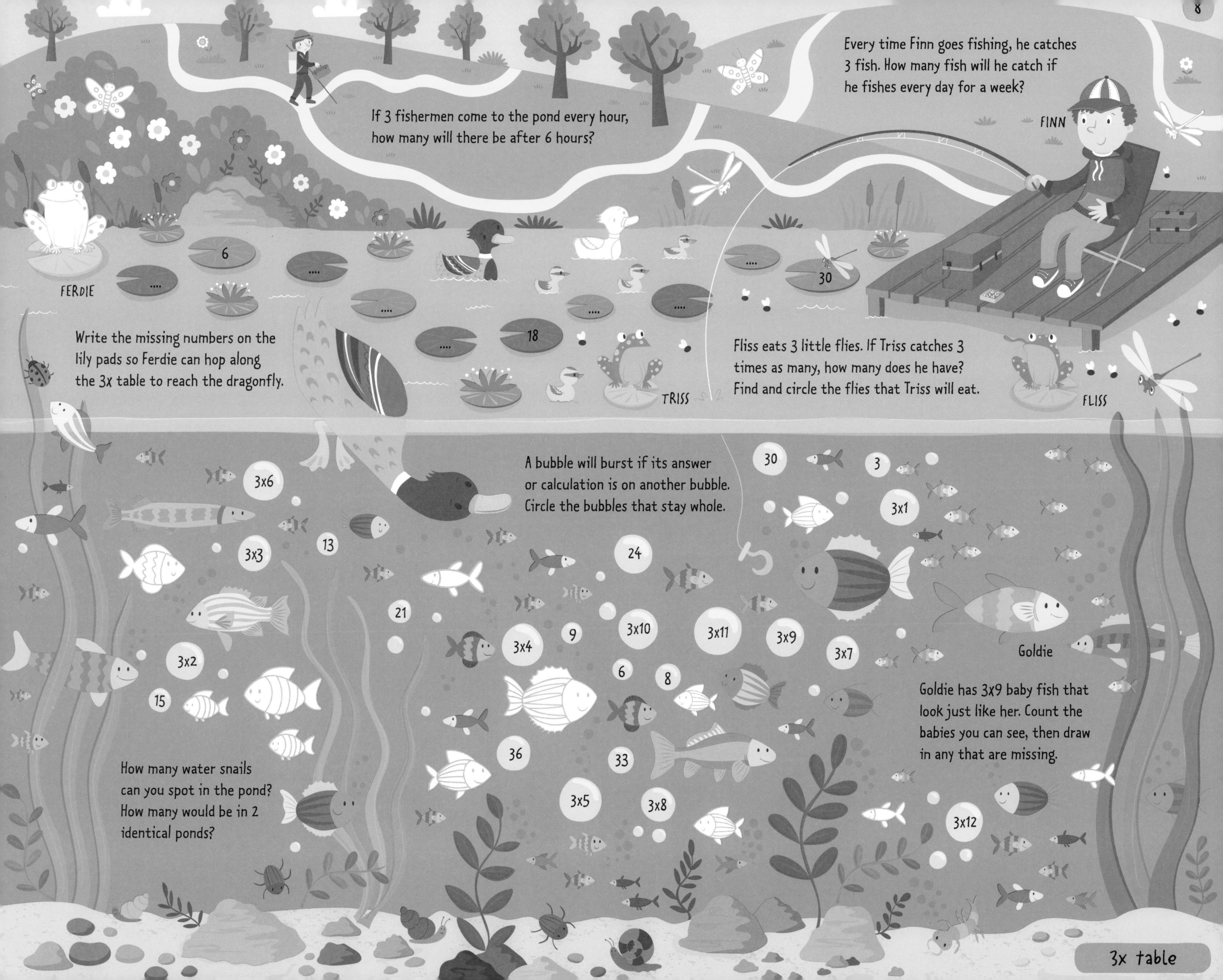

Every time Finn goes fishing, he catches 3 fish. How many fish will he catch if he fishes every day for a week?

FINN

If 3 fishermen come to the pond every hour, how many will there be after 6 hours?

FERDIE

6

18

30

Write the missing numbers on the lily pads so Ferdie can hop along the 3x table to reach the dragonfly.

TRISS

Fliss eats 3 little flies. If Triss catches 3 times as many, how many does he have? Find and circle the flies that Triss will eat.

FLISS

A bubble will burst if its answer or calculation is on another bubble. Circle the bubbles that stay whole.

3x6

3x3

13

3x2

15

21

9

3x4

6

8

24

3x10

3x11

3x9

3x7

30

3

3x1

Goldie

Goldie has 3x9 baby fish that look just like her. Count the babies you can see, then draw in any that are missing.

36

33

3x5

3x8

3x12

How many water snails can you spot in the pond? How many would be in 2 identical ponds?

3x table

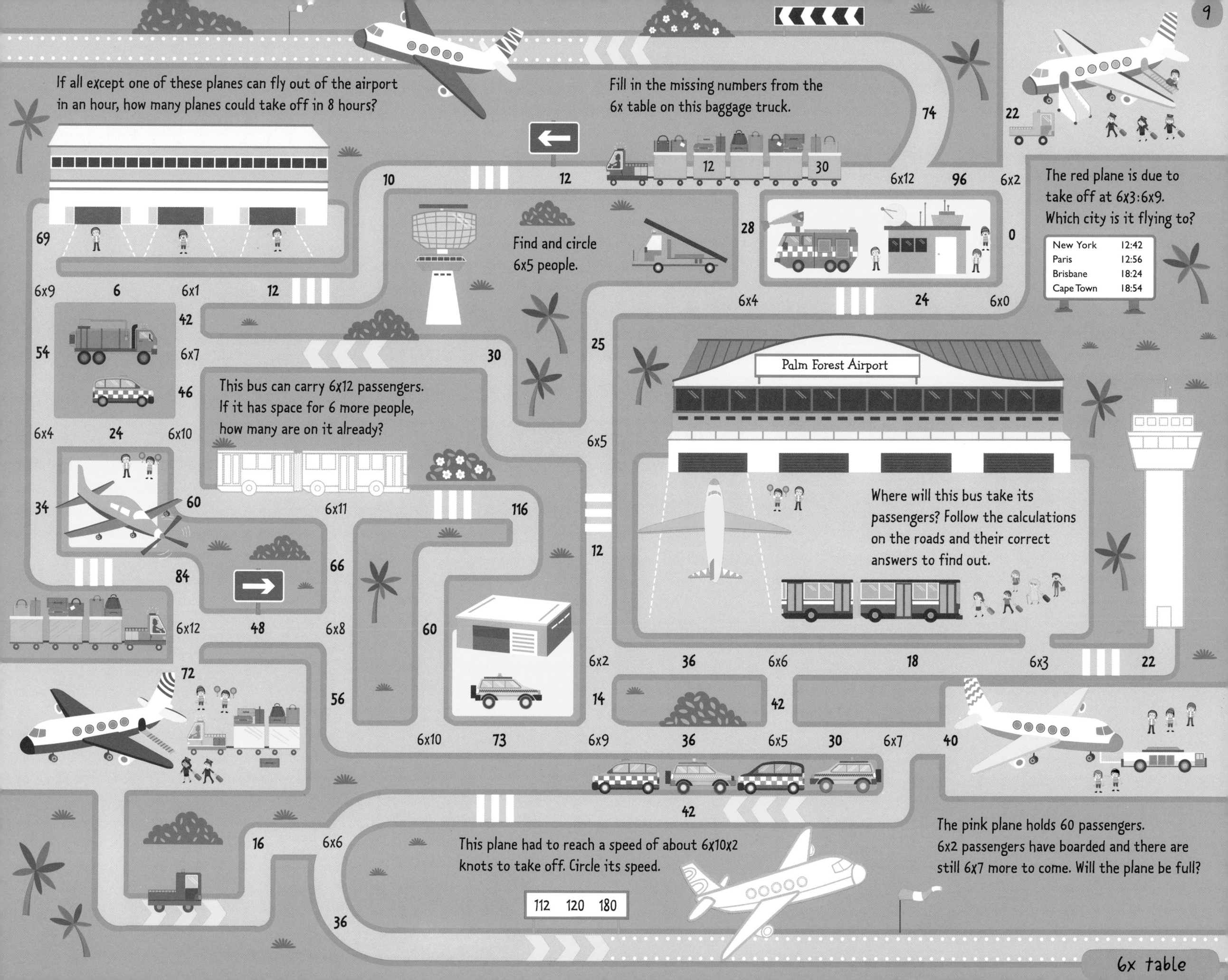

If all except one of these planes can fly out of the airport in an hour, how many planes could take off in 8 hours?

Fill in the missing numbers from the 6x table on this baggage truck.

74   22

12   12   30   6x12   96   6x2

The red plane is due to take off at 6x3:6x9. Which city is it flying to?

New York	12:42
Paris	12:56
Brisbane	18:24
Cape Town	18:54

10   12

28   0

69

Find and circle 6x5 people.

6x9   6   6x1   12

42

54   6x7

46

6x4   24   6x10

This bus can carry 6x12 passengers. If it has space for 6 more people, how many are on it already?

30

25

6x4   24   6x0

6x5

Palm Forest Airport

34   60

84

6x11   116

66

6x12   48   6x8

60

56

Where will this bus take its passengers? Follow the calculations on the roads and their correct answers to find out.

12

72

6x2   36   6x6   18   6x3   22

14   42

6x10   73   6x9   36   6x5   30   6x7   40

42

16   6x6

This plane had to reach a speed of about 6x10x2 knots to take off. Circle its speed.

112   120   180

The pink plane holds 60 passengers. 6x2 passengers have boarded and there are still 6x7 more to come. Will the plane be full?

36

6 fireworks go off every 3 minutes. How many fireworks in a 30-minute display?

Each act is on stage for 3x10 minutes. If there are 6 acts, how many hours does the show last?

Choose 11 people and share 66 glow sticks equally between them, drawing them in their hands.

How many boxes of lightbulbs are needed for all the stage lights, if there are 3 bulbs in each box?

Can you spot 3x4 rabbits?

How many sausages are needed to give 72÷6 people 3 each?

6x8 people are camping in this part of the site. Each tent holds 36÷6 people. Are there enough tents?

3x and 6x tables

7 miners can squeeze into the elevator. How many journeys would it need to take all the workers down the mine?

DANGER! STEEP DROP

7x7=47

7x2=15

7x8=56

7x3=21

7x11=77

7x12=76

7x9=63

7x1=7

If each cart can carry 7 slabs of rock, how many slabs can all the carts hold? 49

Only steps with correct calculations can hold Ed's weight. He needs 6 safe steps to reach the top. Will he make it?

ED

Find and circle 7x1 lanterns and 7x2 shovels. ✓

The elevator travels to the bottom and back in 7 minutes. Circle the number of minutes for 6 journeys.

24   36   42

Dylan is piling up the rocks with numbers in the 7x table. Circle the rocks that will complete the stack.

56
49   14   21
7   42   70   28
84   67   35   53
76

DYLAN

Help Doug find his way to the surface. He can scramble through gaps in the walls and climb up ladders – but only if the number at the top matches the calculation at the bottom.

DOUG

78

84

7x12

35

7x8

70

7x5

54

7x10

14

7x6

63

3

7x2

79

7x9

28

7x11

7x4

7x table

Leon must follow a trail of bubbles with only numbers from the 8x table to reach his friend Leandra. Can you help him find his way?

LEON

30   9   14
62   58   16   18
28   64   22
38   42   34   24   31
6   60   8
76   44   32
52   62   48   42
63   69   56
70   74   40   8
78   24   50
86   90   78
Spot 8x2 yellow fish.
27   80   84
88   98
7
72   19   15
16   18   21
56
96   8
32   34
LEANDRA

$9 \times 12 = 96$

This seahorse has 8x as many babies as you can see here. How many is that? 96

If there were 8 times as many bubbles as jellyfish in this tank, and 8x5 of them burst, how many would be left? Draw in any missing bubbles.

$56 \div 40 = 16$
$8 \times 7 = 56$ $9 \times 5 = 40$

$4 \times 8 = 32$

If there are 8x as many pink fish in this tank as orange fish, how many pink fish are hiding? 32

How many legs do 9 octopuses have? 72

Help the hermit crabs find new homes by matching each calculation to its answer. Then, fill in the missing numbers.

8x11
8x....
88
8x8
48
8x10
80

Solve the puzzles and use their correct answers to steer the *Dancing Williams* safely to the port.

Dead Man's Strait

36

Dancing Williams has 6x8 pirates and 2x8 captives. How many people is that?

Divide 63 golden coins between 7 pirate plunderers.

49

Treasure Cove

The number of days in a 7-week voyage

42

Each lifeboat can hold 6 people. How many are saved?

36

Skull Island

8

9

Sea of Glass

Isle of Hope

56

64

How many pirates could 4 red sea monsters like this catch, grabbing one in each arm?

How many fins do 3 sharks have if one shark has 6?

Share 12 fish between 3 pirates.

6

32

18

11

Thunder Mountain erupts once every 7 years. How many times does it erupt in 84 years?

12

Shark's Teeth

If there are 72 villagers, and the same number in every house, how many live in each?

12

4

Thunder Mountain

24

30

The number of letters in the word COMPASS x 4

10

A cannon fires every 3 minutes. How many cannonballs can it fire in half an hour?

9

28

Buccaneers' Bay

Port Haven

N
W   E
S

3x, 6x, 7x and 8x tables

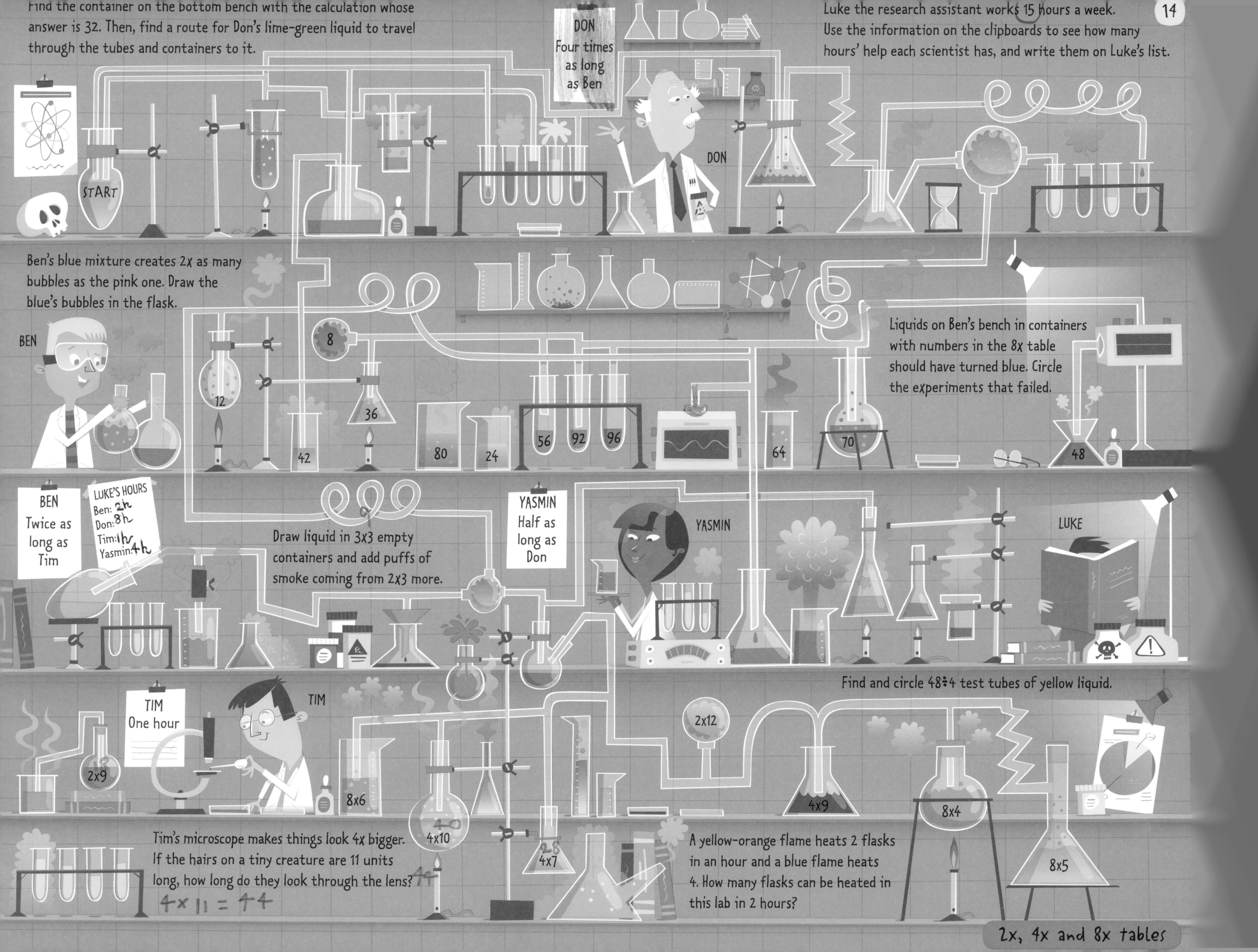

Find the container on the bottom bench with the calculation whose answer is 32. Then, find a route for Don's lime-green liquid to travel through the tubes and containers to it.

DON
Four times as long as Ben

DON

Luke the research assistant works 15 hours a week. Use the information on the clipboards to see how many hours' help each scientist has, and write them on Luke's list.

Ben's blue mixture creates 2x as many bubbles as the pink one. Draw the blue's bubbles in the flask.

BEN

8

12

36

42

Liquids on Ben's bench in containers with numbers in the 8x table should have turned blue. Circle the experiments that failed.

80   24

56   92   96

64

70

48

BEN
Twice as long as Tim

LUKE'S HOURS
Ben: 2h
Don: 8h
Tim: 1h
Yasmin: 4h

Draw liquid in 3x3 empty containers and add puffs of smoke coming from 2x3 more.

YASMIN
Half as long as Don

YASMIN

LUKE

Find and circle 48÷4 test tubes of yellow liquid.

TIM
One hour

TIM

2x9

8x6

2x12

4x9

8x4

4x10

4x7

Tim's microscope makes things look 4x bigger. If the hairs on a tiny creature are 11 units long, how long do they look through the lens?

4 x 11 = 44

A yellow-orange flame heats 2 flasks in an hour and a blue flame heats 4. How many flasks can be heated in this lab in 2 hours?

8x5

2x, 4x and 8x tables

If 9 runners jog around the park in an hour, how many will run around it in 7 hours?

If each squirrel finds 9x1 nuts, how many will they gather altogether?

9x2 people are sitting down. TRUE or FALSE?

If Seth sells 9x as many cups of coffee as ice-cream cones, how many coffees will he sell to these people?

Can you spot 9x4 fallen leaves?

The number of people wearing white tops is 9x _? Find them and fill them in.

If each person with a phone invites 9 friends to the park, how many more people might come?

SETH'S SNACKS

SETH

9x table

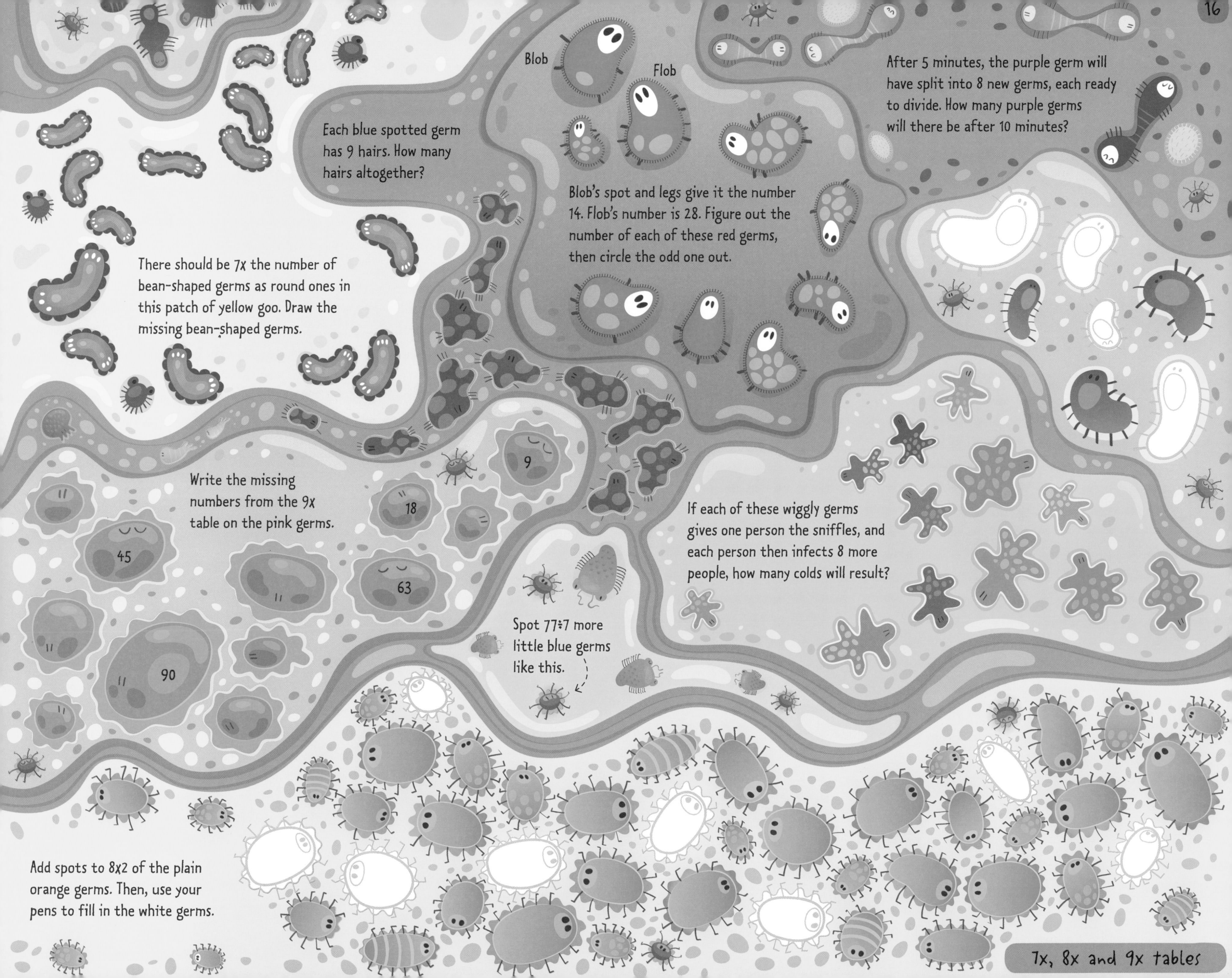

Blob

Flob

Each blue spotted germ has 9 hairs. How many hairs altogether?

After 5 minutes, the purple germ will have split into 8 new germs, each ready to divide. How many purple germs will there be after 10 minutes?

Blob's spot and legs give it the number 14. Flob's number is 28. Figure out the number of each of these red germs, then circle the odd one out.

There should be 7x the number of bean-shaped germs as round ones in this patch of yellow goo. Draw the missing bean-shaped germs.

Write the missing numbers from the 9x table on the pink germs.

9

18

45

63

90

If each of these wiggly germs gives one person the sniffles, and each person then infects 8 more people, how many colds will result?

Spot 77÷7 more little blue germs like this.

Add spots to 8x2 of the plain orange germs. Then, use your pens to fill in the white germs.

7x, 8x and 9x tables

4 men guard each gate and door between this courtyard and the king. There are 10 doors as well as this gate. How many guards altogether?

Light-fingered Len must have 2x11 rotten tomatoes thrown at him. Draw the tomatoes that are waiting to be thrown.

LEN

Join the dots in the order of the 11x table to finish the falconer's tent.

66
77
55
88
11
132
22
121
44
33
110
99

There are 11x as many mice as cats. Can you find them?

Will strikes 11x3 hammer blows every minute. How many blows can he strike in 4 minutes?

A bucket of water is enough to boil turnips for 11 people. Draw any missing buckets needed to cook for twice as many people as you can see.

WILL

Owen has forgotten how to paint the shields. Can you find the paint with the answer to each calculation and fill them in for him?

11x5
11x9
5x11
9x11

11x2x4
9x11
11x3x3
11x8

11x9
11x7
11x8
11x5

7x11
11x5

99
88
55
77

OWEN

ROBIN

Guy Greenarrow's total score was 66. Robin Redarrow's first two arrows scored 33 and 11. If his total score is 132, draw on the target where his other 3 arrows land.

GUY

A barrel holds 11 turnips. How many turnips are in the barrels that Rickon is rolling?

RICKON

CRISPIN'S CAKERY

Can you spot 12x2 red cherries in the picture?

Fill in 12x1 jars.

To make 12 cupcakes, you need 2 eggs. How many cupcakes can you make with the eggs in these boxes?

Paper cases in the 12x table will be filled with chocolate sponge cake. Can you circle them?

This FASTA-BAKE oven bakes a batch of cupcakes in just 12 minutes. How long does it take to bake 12 batches?

FASTA-BAKE

108   96   78   32   60   112   84   56   12   34   48   121   26

PENNY

For every cupcake that fails the quality check, Ken passes 12. If all the decorated cupcakes here failed, how many passed?

QUALITY CONTROL

KEN

A small crate holds 12 boxes of cupcakes and a large crate holds twice as many. How many boxes are in the crates on Jamie's forklift truck?

JAMIE

Penny is piping 12x3 rosebuds on this cake. Doodle blobs to show her where to put the rest of them.

12x table

Can you spot 99÷9 seagulls?

"Captain to Les! Captain to Les! Over. Check the boilers – what's the top speed we can sail at today?"

If the restaurant has 12 tables, each seating up to 4 people, how many people can dine at once?

12x3 people have ordered fish. Circle the crate that needs to be brought up from the store.

12 28 68 96 11 84 38 54 86 144 60 42 78 24 121 72 92 132

Joe is taking bags to cabin 11x6, Elly is delivering to cabin 11x3, Paulo to cabin 11x2 and Des to 11x4. Draw lines to join the porters to the correct cabins.

JOE ELLY PAULO

DES

Only cabins with windows in the 12x table have been booked. Black out the windows of cabins that will be empty on this crossing.

11 22 33

44 55 66

Cars park in lines of 6 with 12 lines on a deck. How many cars can a 2-deck ferry hold?

Write the answers to these calculations on the round windows, then multiply them to see the top speed Les can report to the captain.

72÷12 24÷12 36÷12

LES

Crates with numbers in the 11x table have crabs in them and crates in the 12x table contain fish. Are there more crates of crabs or fish?

88 11 36 STORE

121 84 77 108

144 110 55 120 66

The number of trees in the fairground divided by 11

3

If each bumper car has 11 drivers today, how many bumper-car rides is that?

12

Share 132 ice-cream cones between 11 customers.

11

The number of people wearing hats ÷ 9

12x12 cartons of popcorn

2

63

5

48

110

The number of letters in AMUSEMENT x 7

56

44

3

11 people slide down every minute. How many in 10 minutes?

The number of people on the Ferris wheel if each car holds 4

36

144

122

9

34

11x5 people win a prize playing 'hook a duck'. How many winners is that?

108

How many flowers on 3 bushes if each bush has 12 flowers?

36

96

The number of hot-dog buns in 9 bags of 12

How many swooshes in a 90-second ride if one swoosh takes 9 seconds?

4

22 customers visit in 11 minutes. How many every minute?

65

104

10

8

2

55

6

Divide 72 children equally into 12 groups.

A

B

THE HILLS

THE DALES

The Hill family takes route A and the Dales follow route B. Follow the paths with the correct answers to the puzzles to see where they go. If each clown they meet gives them a balloon, which family collects more balloons?

TICKETS

TICKETS

9x, 11x and 12x tables

JAKE'S BAKES

ROLLS

BUY ANY 6, PAY FOR 3

BAGELS

ROLLS

Jake's baked goods are on special offer. If he sells two thirds of the rolls on display with one sixth of the bagels you can see, how many will he be paid for?

Read Carlo's recipe, then draw his famous celebration cake stack on the empty cake stand below.

CARLO'S CAKE STACK
24÷6 chocolate cakes, each split and filled with: 6÷3 layers of cream with a layer of cherry jam in between. Decorate it as you like with 3x5 cherries.

~ Carlo's Cakes ~

Cake stacks

How high will yours be?

Poppy's Produce

18÷9 pineapples
3x2 apples
45÷9 yellow peppers
12÷6 bunches grapes
72÷12 carrots

Can Libby buy everything on her list? Circle any items she will have to look for somewhere else.

LIBBY

If each little bird at the market eats 3 crusts, how many crusts is that altogether?

BUNTY'S BEAUTIFUL BLOOMS

A Summer Splash bouquet has 3 red, 6 purple and 9 yellow flowers. How many complete bouquets can the florist make today? Draw your own bouquet in the empty bucket.

Back in 3x5 minutes!

BOUQUET OF THE DAY Summer Splash

BUTTERCUP DAIRIES
MILK * CHEESE * EGGS

A large cheese makes 12 portions and a medium cheese, 6 portions. How many portions can be cut from the cheeses on the plates below?

LARGE

MEDIUM

BETTY

There should be enough eggs on Betty's stall to make five 6-egg omelettes. Draw the missing eggs in the basket below.

FRED'S FISHERY

Crabs

Fish

Fred sells 3 times as many purple fish as he sells crabs. Draw the missing purple fish on the tray.

FRESH TO YOU DAILY

3x, 6x, 9x and 12x tables

If it takes 12 weeks to build a house, how many weeks would it take to build 12 houses?

This area will have 6 times as many houses as you can see on Harry's plan. How many houses is that?

Find the two 4-panel squares with answers matching the calculations on the right, and draw around them.

2x2	9x9	8x8	4x4
7x7	5x5	3x3	6x6

1	144	55	81		64	16	4	81
36	64	16	100		49	25	33	0
169	121	4	81		169	9	121	1
0	9	49	25		36	100	144	66

4	81	16	25		169	121	0	1
0	100	1	169		64	16	22	81
77	64	18	121		9	36	49	25
144	9	36	49		144	64	4	100

ELI

MAREK

JOSH

If Marek makes 4x4 mugs of coffee, how many people will not get a drink?

Can you spot 3x3 warning cones?

HARRY

Connect the dots in the order of the square numbers 0x0, 1x1 and so on, to see what Josh is operating. What number should be on the last dot?

9   16   25
36
121   49
100
81   64
4   1   0

Eli is collecting bricks lying around the site. He will pile them in a stack that's the same number of bricks wide as it is high. Draw the stack in the space above.

Square numbers

This asteroid will smash into the planet whose number is 11x12. Write an X on the planet that's in peril.

Find 72÷9 shooting stars.

Fill in the parts of the white rockets as follows:
7x table numbers = red
8x table numbers = yellow
9x table numbers = green

Scout's battery lasts 7x12 hours. Multiply the numbers on each path to see how long it will take, then draw the best route for Scout to reach the flag.

SCOUT

Biff's spacewalk lasted 63÷9 hours, and Jono's was 56÷7 hours. Write an X on the spacecraft of the astronaut whose spacewalk was longer.

Join the dots in the order of the 8x table to finish Stanvat's spaceship.

STANVAT

PIXON

Pixon is beaming a message to Stanvat. It must pass from one satellite to another in the order of the 7x table. Draw blobs on the satellites to show which way Pixon's message will go to reach his friend.

Spot 42÷7 differences between these alien spaceships.

Tricky tables

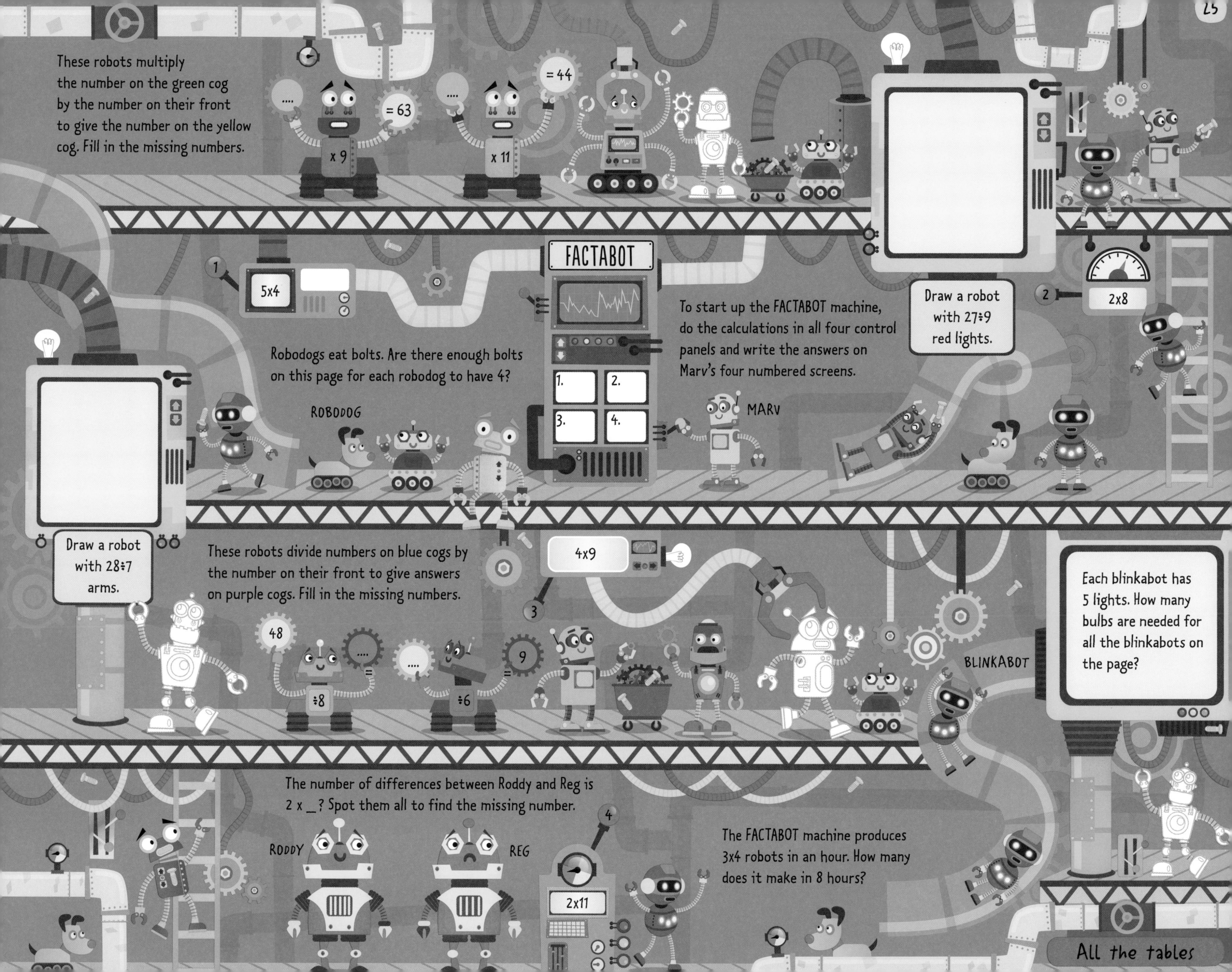

These robots multiply the number on the green cog by the number on their front to give the number on the yellow cog. Fill in the missing numbers.

.... = 63

x 9

.... = 44

x 11

FACTABOT

To start up the FACTABOT machine, do the calculations in all four control panels and write the answers on Marv's four numbered screens.

1.
2.
3.
4.

MARV

Draw a robot with 27÷9 red lights.

1 | 5x4 |

2 | 2x8

Robodogs eat bolts. Are there enough bolts on this page for each robodog to have 4?

ROBODOG

Draw a robot with 28÷7 arms.

These robots divide numbers on blue cogs by the number on their front to give answers on purple cogs. Fill in the missing numbers.

48

....

÷8

....

=

9

÷6

4x9

3

BLINKABOT

Each blinkabot has 5 lights. How many bulbs are needed for all the blinkabots on the page?

The number of differences between Roddy and Reg is 2 x __? Spot them all to find the missing number.

RODDY

REG

4

2x11

The FACTABOT machine produces 3x4 robots in an hour. How many does it make in 8 hours?

All the tables

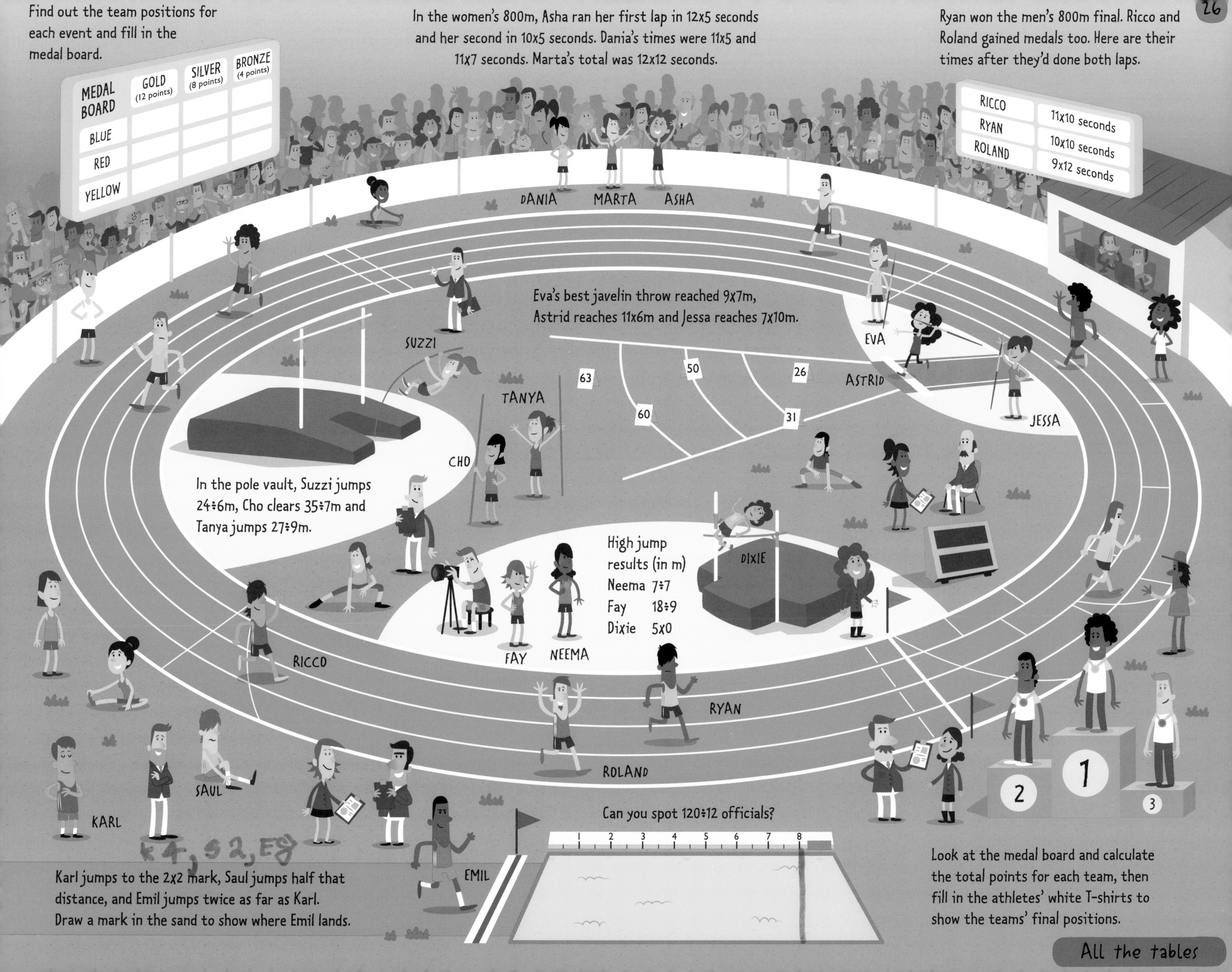

Find out the team positions for each event and fill in the medal board.

MEDAL BOARD

MEDAL BOARD	GOLD (12 points)	SILVER (8 points)	BRONZE (4 points)
BLUE			
RED			
YELLOW			

In the women's 800m, Asha ran her first lap in 12x5 seconds and her second in 10x5 seconds. Dania's times were 11x5 and 11x7 seconds. Marta's total was 12x12 seconds.

Ryan won the men's 800m final. Ricco and Roland gained medals too. Here are their times after they'd done both laps.

RICCO	11x10 seconds
RYAN	10x10 seconds
ROLAND	9x12 seconds

DANIA   MARTA   ASHA

SUZZI

Eva's best javelin throw reached 9x7m, Astrid reaches 11x6m and Jessa reaches 7x10m.

EVA

TANYA

63   50   26

ASTRID

CHO

60   31

JESSA

In the pole vault, Suzzi jumps 24÷6m, Cho clears 35÷7m and Tanya jumps 27÷9m.

High jump results (in m)
Neema 7÷7
Fay   18÷9
Dixie 5x0

DIXIE

FAY   NEEMA

RICCO

RYAN

ROLAND

KARL

SAUL

Can you spot 120÷12 officials?

EMIL

1 2 3 4 5 6 7 8

Karl jumps to the 2x2 mark, Saul jumps half that distance, and Emil jumps twice as far as Karl. Draw a mark in the sand to show where Emil lands.

Look at the medal board and calculate the total points for each team, then fill in the athletes' white T-shirts to show the teams' final positions.

All the tables

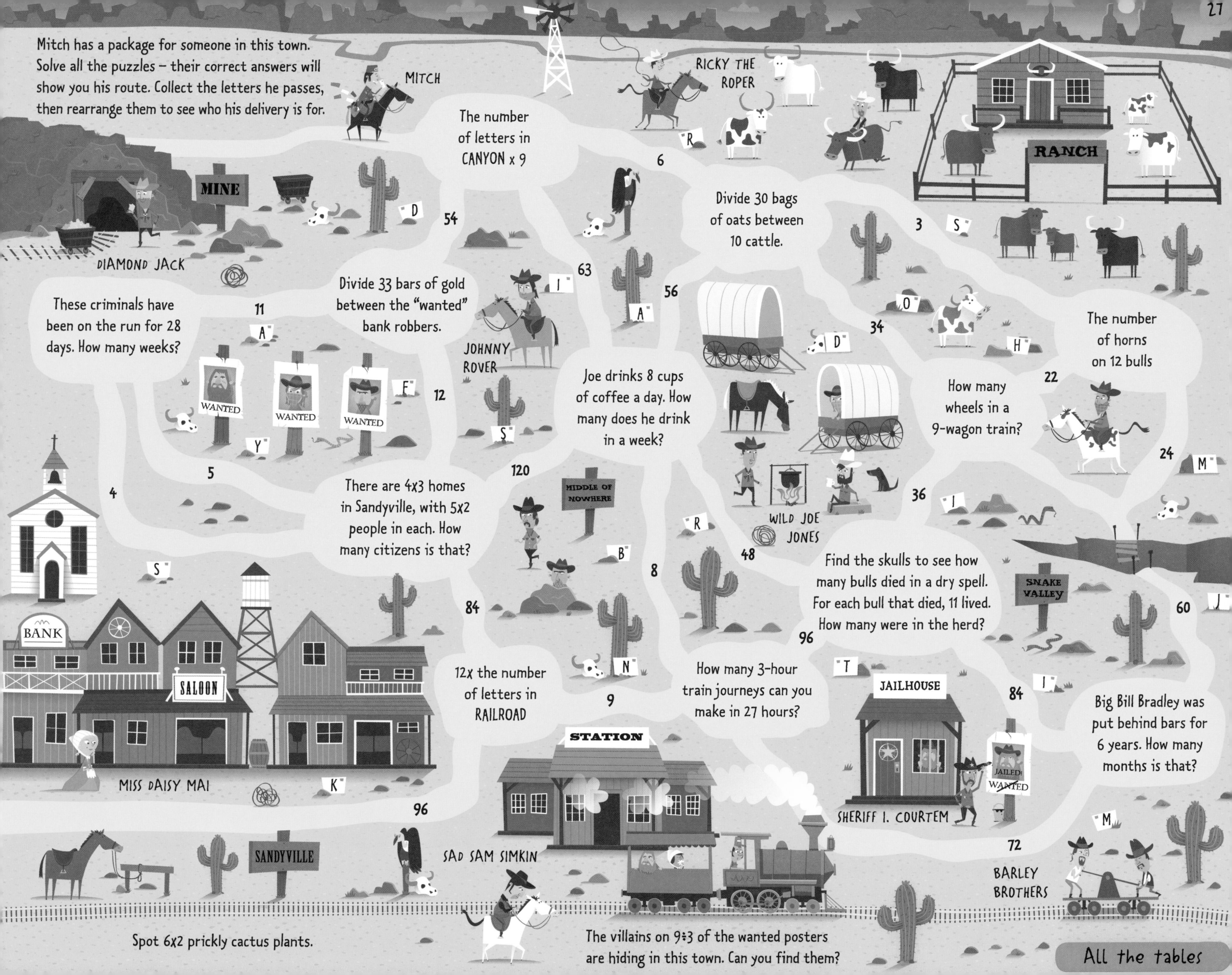

Mitch has a package for someone in this town. Solve all the puzzles – their correct answers will show you his route. Collect the letters he passes, then rearrange them to see who his delivery is for.

MITCH

RICKY THE ROPER

RANCH

The number of letters in CANYON x 9

6

Divide 30 bags of oats between 10 cattle.

3   S

MINE

D

54

O

34

H

DIAMOND JACK

63   I

56   A

Divide 33 bars of gold between the "wanted" bank robbers.

JOHNNY ROVER

The number of horns on 12 bulls

22

These criminals have been on the run for 28 days. How many weeks?

11   A

WANTED   WANTED   WANTED

F   12

Joe drinks 8 cups of coffee a day. How many does he drink in a week?

S

How many wheels in a 9-wagon train?

24   M

Y

5

4   S

There are 4x3 homes in Sandyville, with 5x2 people in each. How many citizens is that?

120

MIDDLE OF NOWHERE

R

WILD JOE JONES

36   I

B

8

48

Find the skulls to see how many bulls died in a dry spell. For each bull that died, 11 lived. How many were in the herd?

SNAKE VALLEY

60   J

BANK

84

N   9

96

T

JAILHOUSE

84   I

SALOON

12x the number of letters in RAILROAD

How many 3-hour train journeys can you make in 27 hours?

Big Bill Bradley was put behind bars for 6 years. How many months is that?

MISS DAISY MAI

K

STATION

SHERIFF I. COURTEM

96

JAILED! WANTED

M

72

SANDYVILLE

SAD SAM SIMKIN

BARLEY BROTHERS

Spot 6x2 prickly cactus plants.

The villains on 9÷3 of the wanted posters are hiding in this town. Can you find them?

All the tables

MAXIMUM
PEOPLE

There should be 56÷8 snowmen.
Draw the ones that are missing.

If each cable car can hold 4x2 people, what is the
maximum number of people who can travel by cable
car at once? Write the answer on the warning sign.

If 11x as many skiers
as snowboarders visit
the resort today, how
many skiers is that?

Multiply the
numbers on each
route to see who
skied down in the
shortest time.

2
2
3
1
2
5
11
12

38
27
99
45
56
74
24
36
63
19
9   KEV   JAYNE   18

SVEN   STEFAN

ERIK'S EQUIPMENT

ERIK

SKIS
SKATES

Jayne and Kev's chalet is at the
end of the path that only has
numbers from the 9x table
on it. Circle their chalet.

CAFÉ

So far today, Erik has rented out 12x
as many pairs of skis as pairs of
skates. How many pairs of skis is that?

HOTEL

Do the calculations to
see how many cases are
in the snow truck.

42÷7   36÷9

All the tables

Starting in the bottom left square, follow the instructions to complete the crystal quest.

29

1 x 1 =	1		2 x 1 =	2		3 x 1 =	3		4 x 1 =	4		5 x 1 =	5		6 x 1 =	6
1 x 2 =	2		2 x 2 =	4		3 x 2 =	6		4 x 2 =	8		5 x 2 =	10		6 x 2 =	12
1 x 3 =	3		2 x 3 =	6		3 x 3 =	9		4 x 3 =	12		5 x 3 =	15		6 x 3 =	18
1 x 4 =	4		2 x 4 =	8		3 x 4 =	12		4 x 4 =	16		5 x 4 =	20		6 x 4 =	24
1 x 5 =	5		2 x 5 =	10		3 x 5 =	15		4 x 5 =	20		5 x 5 =	25		6 x 5 =	30
1 x 6 =	6		2 x 6 =	12		3 x 6 =	18		4 x 6 =	24		5 x 6 =	30		6 x 6 =	36
1 x 7 =	7		2 x 7 =	14		3 x 7 =	21		4 x 7 =	28		5 x 7 =	35		6 x 7 =	42
1 x 8 =	8		2 x 8 =	16		3 x 8 =	24		4 x 8 =	32		5 x 8 =	40		6 x 8 =	48
1 x 9 =	9		2 x 9 =	18		3 x 9 =	27		4 x 9 =	36		5 x 9 =	45		6 x 9 =	54
1 x 10 =	10		2 x 10 =	20		3 x 10 =	30		4 x 10 =	40		5 x 10 =	50		6 x 10 =	60
1 x 11 =	11		2 x 11 =	22		3 x 11 =	33		4 x 11 =	44		5 x 11 =	55		6 x 11 =	66
1 x 12 =	12		2 x 12 =	24		3 x 12 =	36		4 x 12 =	48		5 x 12 =	60		6 x 12 =	72

7 x 1 =	7		8 x 1 =	8		9 x 1 =	9		10 x 1 =	10		11 x 1 =	11		12 x 1 =	12
7 x 2 =	14		8 x 2 =	16		9 x 2 =	18		10 x 2 =	20		11 x 2 =	22		12 x 2 =	24
7 x 3 =	21		8 x 3 =	24		9 x 3 =	27		10 x 3 =	30		11 x 3 =	33		12 x 3 =	36
7 x 4 =	28		8 x 4 =	32		9 x 4 =	36		10 x 4 =	40		11 x 4 =	44		12 x 4 =	48
7 x 5 =	35		8 x 5 =	40		9 x 5 =	45		10 x 5 =	50		11 x 5 =	55		12 x 5 =	60
7 x 6 =	42		8 x 6 =	48		9 x 6 =	54		10 x 6 =	60		11 x 6 =	66		12 x 6 =	72
7 x 7 =	49		8 x 7 =	56		9 x 7 =	63		10 x 7 =	70		11 x 7 =	77		12 x 7 =	84
7 x 8 =	56		8 x 8 =	64		9 x 8 =	72		10 x 8 =	80		11 x 8 =	88		12 x 8 =	96
7 x 9 =	63		8 x 9 =	72		9 x 9 =	81		10 x 9 =	90		11 x 9 =	99		12 x 9 =	108
7 x 10 =	70		8 x 10 =	80		9 x 10 =	90		10 x 10 =	100		11 x 10 =	110		12 x 10 =	120
7 x 11 =	77		8 x 11 =	88		9 x 11 =	99		10 x 11 =	110		11 x 11 =	121			
7 x 12 =	84		8 x 12 =	96		9 x 12 =	108		10 x 12 =	120					

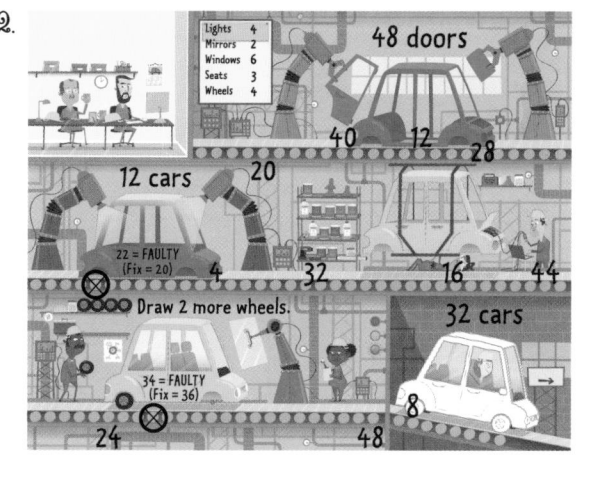

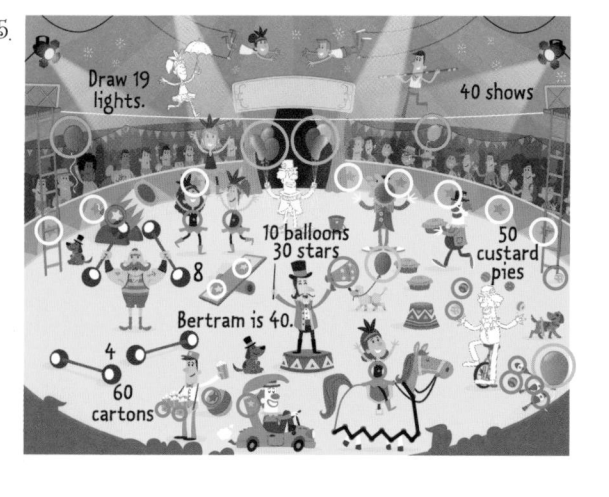
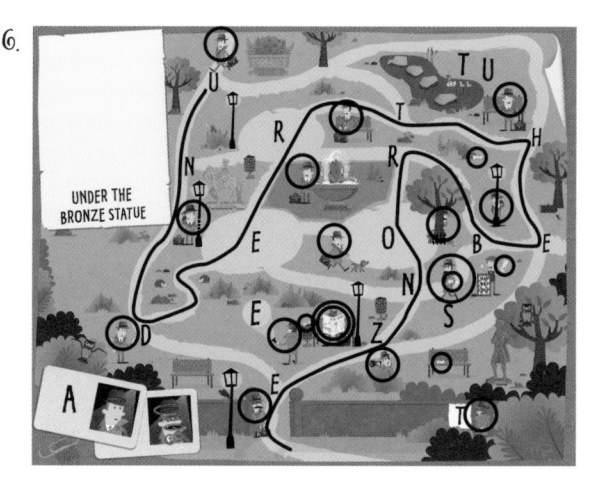
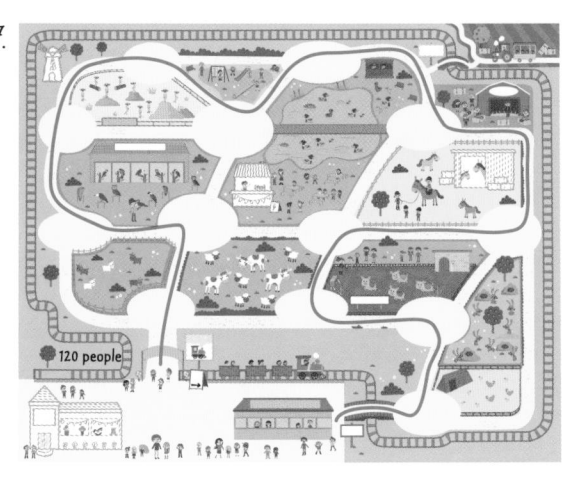
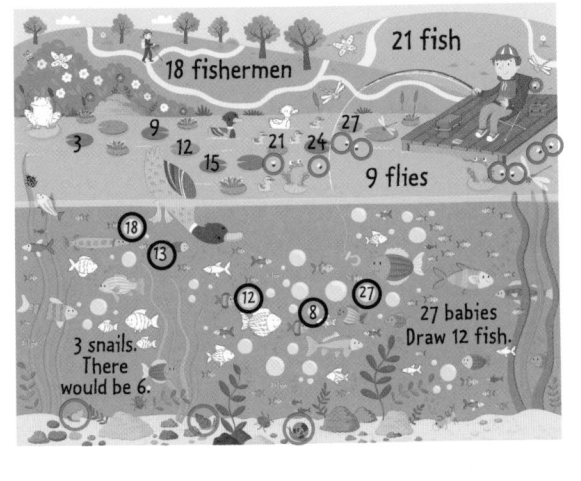
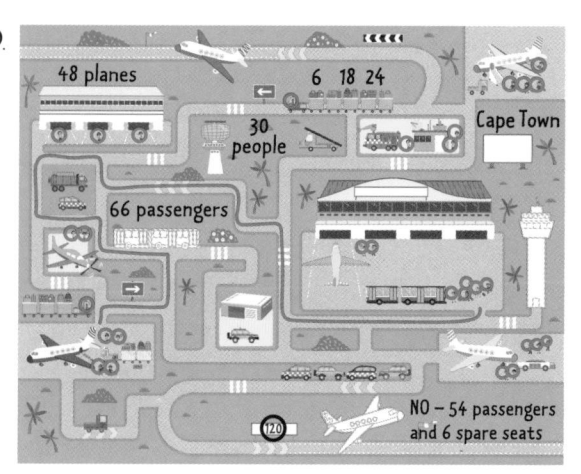

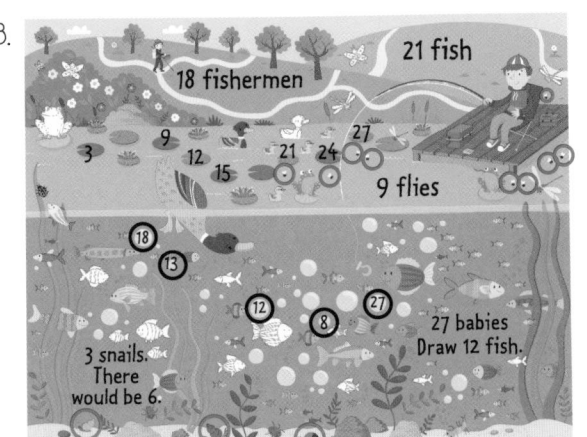
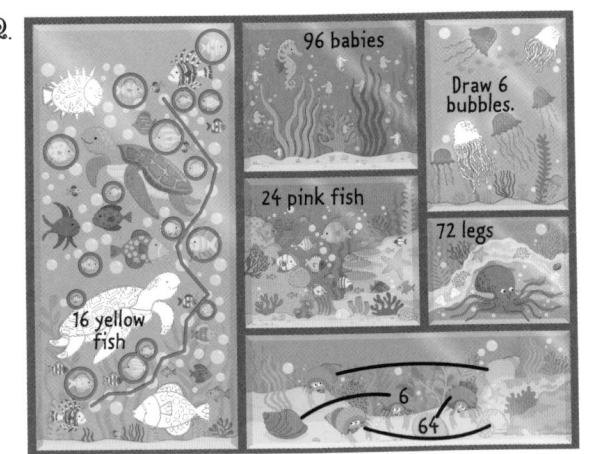

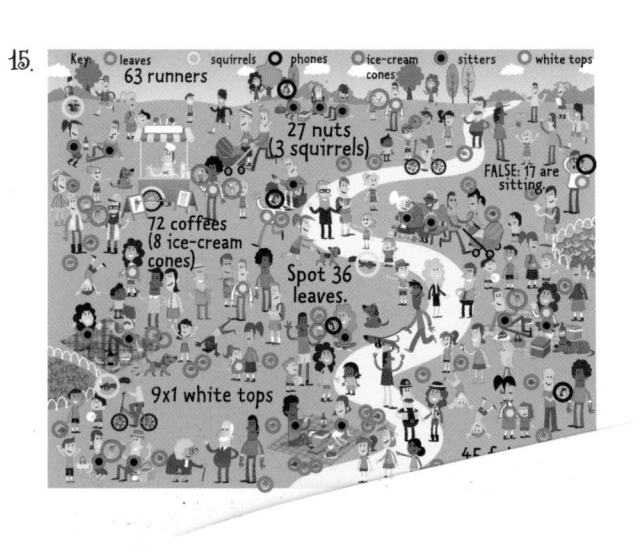
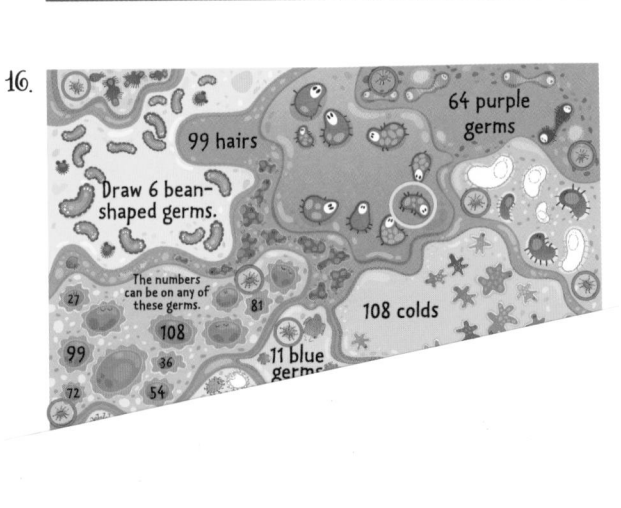

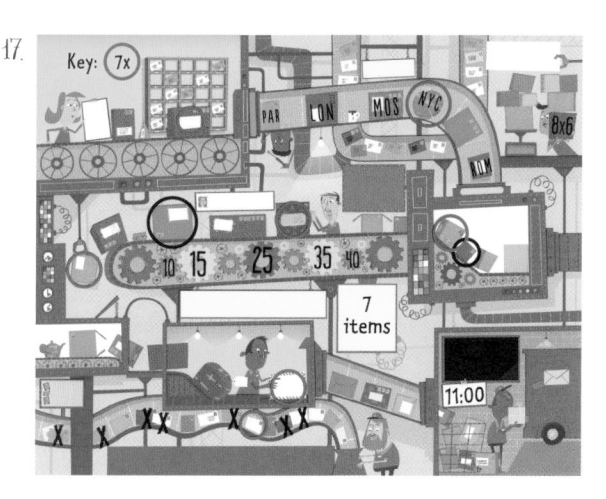
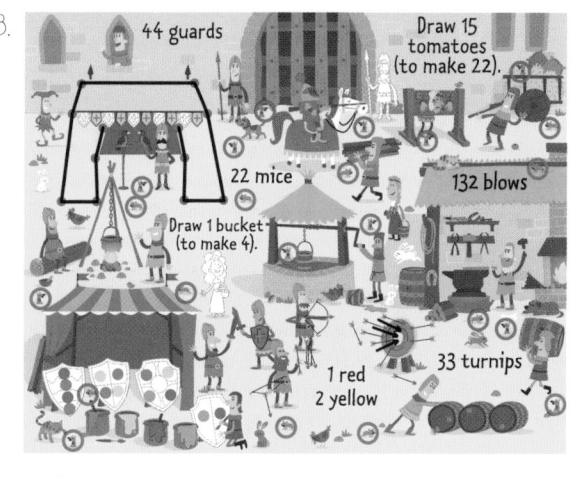
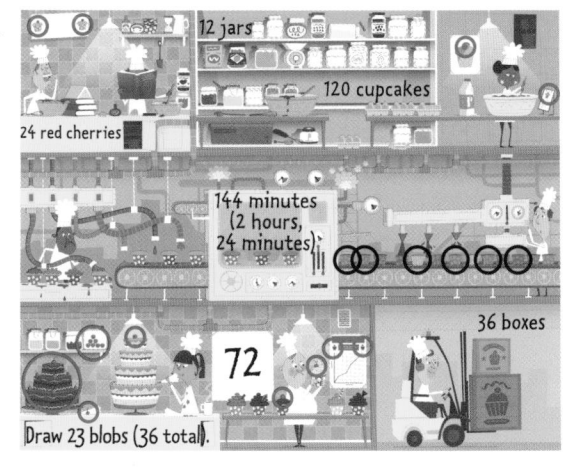
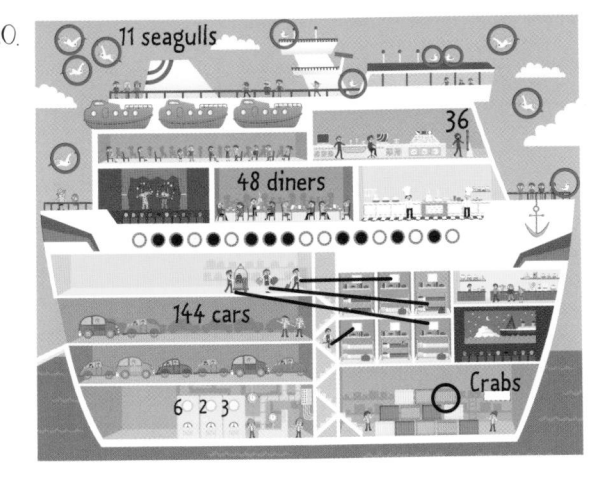

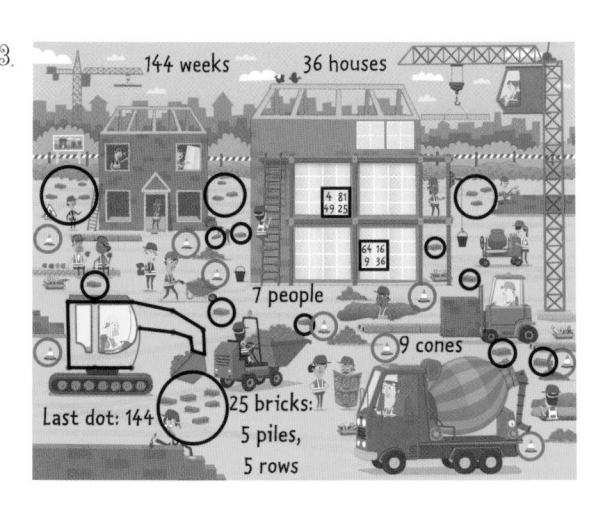
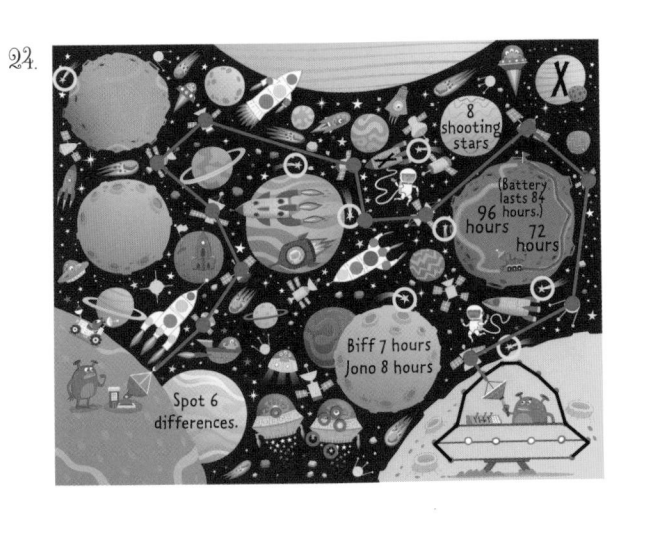
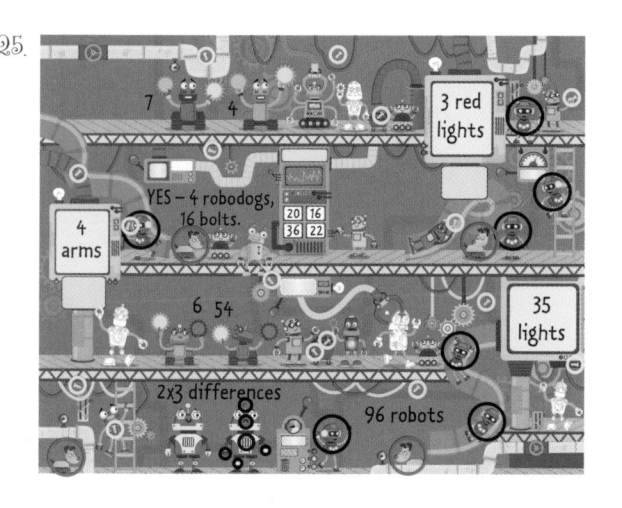
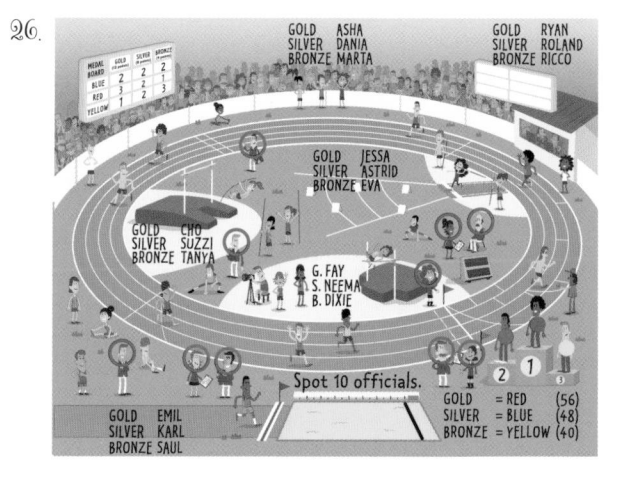